...AR
...D OTHER STUFF

BY
GIOVANNI
'SPOZ'
ESPOSITO

ILLUSTRATIONS BY

COLIN FAULKNER
CARL THOMPSON
AND
PAUL HILL

A BOSTIN ... BLICATION

First published in the United Kingdom in 2008 by

Bostin Productions
107 Cliff Rock Road,
Rednal,
Birmingham
B45 8QF

www.spoz.net

Cover design and layout by Carl Thompson and Spoz

ISBN 13 : 978-0-9560645-0-9

Printed and bound by CPI Antony Rowe, Eastbourne

U.K. £7.99 RRP

Acknowledgements

Some of the poems in this book have popped up in an assortment of places, before appearing on these pages.

A Sticky World was first published in **Rhyme and Reason** by United Press (2003).

Philip Guise and His X-Ray Eyes, Disco Dad, The Day the Earth Grew Hair, Spaceships, Food and *A Sticky World* all appeared on Spoz's CD **Poetry in Motions** (2004).

I've also lost count of the numbers of websites (as well as which ones) that have   displayed some of these poems within their virtual pages. Thank you ... all of you.

Whilst Arts Council (West Midlands) have not funded this book in any way, they did give me a big "bunk up" when I first got started with this freelance poet thing. Many thanks for all your help folks!

Contents

4

For Claudia,
Francesca
and Zack

Disco Dad

Disco dad is on the floor,
He's had a drink … or three or four,
The guests are heading for the door,
As disco dad puts lives at risk,
He twists and nearly slips his disc.
He's going to put his back out,
He's going to have a black out
And embarrass me even more than he *is* doing…
His toupee needs a bit of gluing,
As he jumps and jives in his blue suede shoe … ing.

Disco dad don't care for fashion,
Got his flares from the local cash 'n' … carry,
With his best mate Barry,
Whose dress sense is as bad as his.
"You kids don't know what real music is!
Back in my day, bands could play,
None of this techno … techno …techno … notice."
Yes dad,
Thanks dad.
Now shut up and sit down before we put you in a home.

Welcome to Birmingham – Have a Nice Day!

Brum in the sixties, some say "Those were the days",
A superior city in so many ways,
'Cause the streets were paved with faggots and 'pays'.
Welcome to Birmingham – have a nice day.

Enoch Powell came and gave us 'Rivers of Blood',
He was bad, he was ugly and he wasn't that good,
'Cause we were more tolerant in our neighbourhood
Welcome to Birmingham – have a nice day

Our city was shaken in seventy four,
By evil men trying to settle a score,
Perhaps a sign of futures we'd all have to endure?
Welcome to Birmingham – have a nice day.

In came the Eighties with ole' Maggie Thatcher,
Gave us inflation, unemployment and the kiddie's milk snatcher.
Though some people tried, they just couldn't dispatch her.
Welcome to Birmingham – have a nice day.

The nineties were grey, then 'TB' came along,
He tried to put right all the things that were wrong,
With a big cheesy grin and a nice Brit Pop song.
Welcome to Birmingham – have a nice day.

Now the 'noughties' are nice, we've been going through changes,
Our city's been growing like Alpine mountain ranges,
With that Selfridges building – the epitome of what strange is.
Welcome to Birmingham – have a nice day.

We know we're not perfect, but we're having a go,
At least we've made progress, even if it *is* slow,
Because every great oak takes a long time to grow.
Welcome to Birmingham – have a nice day.

House Fly (inspired by Paul Hill)

You know me.
Musca Domestica they call me in Latin.
Makes me sound smart, so I had to get that in,
Urrrrg! What's that you've sat in?
My dinner, that's what.
I come out in the cold, but I prefer it hot,
From white egg to maggot, I hide to pupate,
Then emerge as this creature you all love to hate ...
...that's it ... I am ... the house fly.

Are you even remotely interested?
I have to drool on my dinner to ensure it's digested!
From grilled chicken goujons,
To gravy and grit,
All I have to do is ... spit.
And if spotted, I'm swatted,
Or zapped out of existence,
But you've got to admire my pesky persistence.

All us house flies
Have compound eyes,
We are god-like, we are all seeing,
Quite impressive for a little being.
A hundred eyes will see you coming,
Because I, I, I, I ... eye ... get the picture?...
... am the house fly.

My neighbourhood really stinks, so please
Be gentle as I spread disease,
I've been known to bring villages to their knees
And I've often had my cholera felt,
My dysentery hits below the belt...
Typhoid, T.B. , salmonella,
I'm a dirty little fella,
But it's what I do! Don't question why,
Because I ... am the house fly.

Yeah, yeah, yeah ... it's easy to frown
At the filthy fly and look down ... on me,
But this is the body I was born in,
A vessel forlorn for you all to pour scorn in,
But there's a new day dawnin' ...
All is not ... as it seems,
'Cause I too ... like you ... have dreams.
Dreams that some say, are above my station,
Though, on paper, my aspiration
Is not such a wild and drastic mutation.
Just give me a minute, give me some time
And I'll speak of my longing for a life without grime,
A life free of filth, the bog and the gutter,
A fly that is prefixed, not with 'house'...
... but with 'butter'.

You see? I'm literally half way there!
A slip of the tongue, a sleight of hand,
Would make me elegant, fine and grand.
From pole to pole, beyond equator,
An economically valued pollinator,
Esteemed and easy on the eye,
Yes ... I could be ... a butterfly.

Look ... there goes one now - such heirs and graces,
Putting smiles on peoples' faces,
No one swats ... no one's scowling,
That fly's as rich as ... J.K.Rowling.
Just look at those 'Tiffany' lampshade wings,
Not like my transparent, stumpy things,
Oh! To float and fleet and flutter,
Far from faeces, gunge and gutter.
Doesn't it make you want to cry?
I would die ... to be ... a butterfly.

Just look ... how creatures from all around,
Are drawn to the sight that has no sound.
From sparrows to spiders, and tabbies to toads,
If you want attention, then you've got loads!
You just can't hide even if you try ...
When you're a dainty, painted butterfly!

Hmmm ... now there's a thought ...
When blessed with wings of such a colourful pallet,
It's like ringing the 'lunch time' bell ...with a mallet!
That promise of beauty turns horribly bleak,
When confronted by a finch's beak!
When you're perched on petals, supping nectar,
You could easily be trapped by a butterfly collector!
Pinned to a board and put on display,
That's not my idea of a wonderful day!

And see ... a sporadic wind or gust,
Defies the butterfly's feeble thrust!
An overly zealous breeze or zephyr,
Sends it stumbling like a new born heifer!
That's not too clever...
Butterflies? Yeah ... whatever ...

Perhaps my dream was ill conceived,
Who'd have believed ... I wasn't inferior ...
The days I've grieved ... for my hackneyed exterior,
Don't be deceived ... yes, it's me ... the superior,
I'm coarse and abrupt, I can't deny,
I've spat on my fair share of humble pie,
The gastricly challenged ... need not apply,
You can rely ... on my notoriety,
Because I ... am a fly ...
Of the HOUSE variety!

13

Spaceships

Angela Vickers flashes her knickers,
To all of the farmer's strawberry pickers,
As she leapt over the stile…without much style or grace,
While I picked strawberries with a smile on my face,
In the strawberry field that had been there forever.

Well … at least since last year.
Because the year before that, it was a field full of wheat,
Where Angela played with my best friend, Pete.
They made shapes, her and Pete, in the wheat with their feet,
To make people think visitors from space had been
Meeting and greeting our planet.
It can't be true, can it ?

Well, they had … in a field next to that one,
In a thin silver spaceship, or was it a fat one ?
Pete only knows, 'cause they took him away,
Well they must have, 'cause I haven't seen him since that day.
They whisked him up into the milky way
And fed him Galaxy bars … or even a Mars
As they battled with spaceships … up there in the stars.

He could be there now … exchanging blows with Darth Vader,
Or impressing Princess Leia
With some clothes that he made her
(Pete always told us, time after time,
He longed for a future in fashion design).

When will he come back ? Or will he want to ?
An adventure like that would be great to hold on to.
One day he'll return a success, not a failure,
From that far away planet,
The one called Australia.

I Can't Rap

I'm no good at rapping, I just can't rap,
When it comes to rapping, I'm ... no good,
I can't get down with my "homies" in "da hood",
I'm no good at rapping – is that understood?

I don't know any rappers, I can't name them,
Fifty Pence? Acorn? Oh yeah – there's Eminem!
I don't spit bars, I just spit phlegm,
Snoop Dog's not for me – I prefer REM.

I know it sounds boring, I know it sounds sad
And I know that you can rap, even if you are a dad,
But I just get frustrated and a little bit mad,
'Cause when people say I'm "bad", they mean plain bad.

I could never be wicked 'cause rapping's too hard,
My tongue gets tied and my rhymes get jarred,
If rapping was a club then I'd be barred,
If rapping was football, I'd get a red card.

I sound a real fool when I yell "Brap! Brap!"
In my Argos bling and my baseball cap,
I woke up my granny, who was having a nap,
She said "Stop that noise or I'll give you a slap!"

I'm no good at rapping, I ain't got "da flow",
I'm talking about a toy when I say "Yo! Yo!"
I can't rap fast and I can't rap slow,
"Is Spoz a rapper?" The answer's "no".

16

<u>Wrapping on my Presents</u>

Yo!... Yo man! Check this out ...
I'm sure this ain't what Christmas is supposed to be about,
I got big ones, small ones, short and long,
I think this one's a video, I could be wrong,
Hey look! It's a book, I mistook it's shape,
For an out of date cassette full of video tape.
I want a game or three for my PS2,
Well I've gone and got a DVD of 'Scooby Doo'!
Now Christmas comes but once a year,
I hope that all the presents that I want are here,
'Cause if they're not, I won't get a lot too soon,
My birthday doesn't come around until next June!
"Hey kid don't be ungrateful",
Shout my mum and dad,
"You've got so many presents that we never had!
Christmas ain't about the presents in your stocking,
It's been twisted out of shape,
We find it rather shocking...
Christmas is the story
'Bout the birth of Jesus,
And let us tell you something that would really please us,
If you took your presents
And shared them out,
Among the kids in this world
Who've been given ...
Nowt.

17

Dolphin Bubble

Dolphin bubble,
Belly dancing,
All the way to the top,
When it breaks the ocean surface,
It's going to go 'pop'.
When it breaks the ocean surface,
It's going to make a noise,
Like the one the dolphin made
With all the dolphin girls and boys;
At the school
Where all the dolphins go,
Where they're taught,
"It's not the size of bubble you blow,
Just so long as
You're forever blowing bubbles,
And your bubbles
Don't cause trouble,
But leave a ripple".

Rock Hard Striker

The keeper's having a nightmare,
The striker's ten foot tall!
He's charging like a monster,
As he goes up for the ball!
The striker's elbow's jutting out,
To catch the keeper's chin,
The monster striker's full of menace,
Gnashing teeth and manic grin.
The keeper takes a knock,
The striker's made of rock!
The referee's not seen a thing,
'Cause he was pulling up his sock!
The keeper reels around in pain,
As the ball goes in the net again.
Half time can't come soon enough,
The keeper's had his fill,
Oh no...here comes another shot...
It's twenty seven – nil.

Washing Machine

My mum had a washing machine,
That washed things incredibly clean,
Then one day by mistake,
When it started to shake,
It turned all our underwear green.

In a colour book, with
colour illustrations, the
underwear would be
green.

20

When Rover, Our Dog, Went Mental

The dog's gone flippin' mental!
He's gone and bit my hand!
He's trying to bury my brother
And his best friend in the sand!
Old Rover's nicked the car keys
And he's heading for the door,
With the A to Z between his teeth
And the 'crook lock' in his paw.
His tail's a wagging frantically,
His eyes are rolling over,
It's sad to see a mental dog,
Especially when it's Rover.
He used to be so happy,
Chasing sticks and chewing conkers;
He really was a man's best friend,
But now he's flippin' bonkers.

Big Cats

Big cats are only big,
If you are smaller than them.
When a bike has got two seats,
It's sometimes called a tandem.
You'll never win the lottery
Because it's purely random.
You could get splinters from old floor boards,
Unless you really sand 'em.

Wildlife Adoption

You ought to care for animals,
'Cause they would care for you.
They'd put you in a sanctuary,
Or in a human zoo.
So when you see a sign that says,
'Adopt a lion or monkey'
Say 'YES! I REALLY WANT TO HELP!'
...But what if their parents come back for them?

Sherlock Holmes Poem

Why is the front door on Sherlock Holmes's home bright yellow?
Why didn't he paint it blue with orange spots on?
I guess that would have made it uncharacteristically lewd,
As it is, it's a lemon entry my dear Watson.

Sherlock Holmes was prescribed some medicated tablets,
After a bite from the Hound of the Baskervilles.
So he went down to the chemist with a tenner and his 'Thermos'
And came back with a pound and a flask o' pills.

Insomnia

Mom! Hey mom!
I can't get to sleep,
I've tried counting hedgehogs
And rabbits and sheep.
I think I'm excited, Or maybe afraid,
I've even been chatting with God as I prayed.
He said not to worry as things would be fine,
but I'm still wide awake, and God...
... look at the time!
The 'Horlicks' ain't worked,
I'm as fresh as a daisy,
The sand man's on strike, or he's ever so lazy.
...Now I'm getting tired of not being...tired,
Even the bugs in my bed have expired,
I need to nod off, it would help such a heap,
But it just isn't fun, when you ...
can't get...
to ...
...sleep.

A Sticky World

Stick men
And sticky women
Wear great big sticky
Trunks to swim in.
Sticky dogs
Chase sticky sticks,
'Round sticky houses,
Built of sticky bricks.
Sticky kids with sticky faces…
Brians, Sarahs, Colins, Tracies.
Sticky limbs
That break and scrape,
Stuck back together with
Sticky tape.
Sticky insects eat
Sticky grubs.
Sticky beer in
Sticky pubs.
Lots of sticky lies
Could lead to a sticky situation.
Sticky Roger Daltreys sing
'My sticky generation'.
Sticky stamps on sticky letters
Sent to your best stick friend,
Keep your sticky fingers clean,
Don't meet a sticky end.
Sticky bats and balls for cricket,
With sticky stumps
On a sticky wicket
Sticky hospitals for the sick,
What's brown and sticky?
A stick.

A Stretchy World

Stretchy socks and stretchy pants,
Stretchy trunks on elephants.
Stretchy trunks in the swimming pool,
Stretching gum is really cool.
Stretch a three to make a four,
Go down for a stretch if you break the law.
If you get hurt, someone'll fetch yer
And carry you off on a first aid stretcher.
Don't stretch a budget,
Don't stretch resources,
Stretch your imagination instead
And enrol on some evening courses.

The Day the Earth Grew Hair

T'was a crispy morn, 'bout an hour past dawn,
As the sun had snuck past the horizon,
I squinted to see what time it was
And remembered I didn't have my eyes on.
So I grabbed hold of my specs and in a couple of secs,
I beheld a sight beyond compare,
There it stood in it's morning glory,
The earth outside covered in hair.

The landscape was strewn like a hairy baboon,
You could almost reach out and pull it,
There were beehives that looked like a beehive
And a park bench that looked like a mullet.
I put out a call to my bald neighbour, Paul,
"Isn't it so bloomin' typical" I said,
"The stuff seems to be sprouting everywhere,
Except on the place called your head."

It was unfair hair, that hair over there,
It would need a trim well before noon,
So rather than phoning the council,
I phoned up for Vidal Sasoon.
He was a hell of a stylist, he was short on our high list
And they say that the man never quits,
Which was just as well for our hair covered earth,
As I spotted some ten inch high nits.

In the blink of an eye, Vidal took to the sky
In his jumbo jet hair styling shears,
He whizzed around cutting the Earth's hair,
Taking care not to snip the Earth's ears.
So the deed had been done and the day had been won,
Vidal was praised by the land's premier...
And the world went on doing what it had been doing,
The day before the Earth grew hair.

Ten and a Half

I was the second hard of the juniors,
Fancying girls in my class wasn't cool,
Especially the one with the glasses,
So I resorted to playing the fool.
I pulled on your pigtails when I longed to pull you,
My wooing technique was appalling,
I longed to embrace you, but I couldn't face you,
So I made do with childish name calling.
Oh 'stinky bum' we were only ten,
There was no chance of romance,
For I could never call you 'my sweetheart',
Only 'specky four eyes poo poo pants'.
That was one of the many names
That I would pluck out from the air,
Name after name, oh the sin, oh the shame,
Every name except your name – 'Claire'.
Lovely Claire, gentle Claire,
Were you ever remotely aware
That every hair on your head had me rolling in bed,
Had me grinning from 'ere to there.
I could only muster school boy pranks
Instead of mustering kisses or hugs,
I should have given you chocolates or flowers,
Instead of filling your satchel with bugs.
Claire, lovely Claire, you know life wasn't fair,
Though, I hoped, when we grew, we'd get 'pally'...
No, it wasn't to be, for in junior three
A new girl had started called 'Sally'.
Oh, Sally the lovely, Sally the gentle,
Did you know that your legs, hair and face drove me mental.
I tried to behave more maturely,
I tried to give you a bit of a laugh,
But you just called me 'stinky'
And 'wee willie winky'
After all, we were ten – and a half.

Specs

Call me four eyes,
I don't care,
'Cause I like to wear
My pair
Of specs.
Contact lenses aren't my thing,
'Cause specs won't make my eyes sore.
I have two eyes.
My specs make four.
I feel no need to be ashamed,
'Cause like my lenses,
You've been framed.

Robert Denham

Robert Denham skateboard ace,
Took his skateboard all over the place,
Down the shops and round the park,
In the daytime, in the dark,
He rode it places he should not
And turn three sixty on the spot
We'd sit and watch him – flippin' 'eck!
How does he do that with his deck!
He'd do wheelies and hops and stunts and tricks
On his home made skateboard in 1976.

Food

It's rude to play with your food said mum,
As my brother Pete bowled me a sprout.
It's rude to play with your food,
What's more,
If you don't stop it now,
I shall give you what for!
But it was too late.
The peas on my plate
Were ripe for a swipe from my cricket bat knife,
As I whacked one for four ...
...And the sprout for a six,
Sadly the boundary was Dad's 'Weetabix'.
The umpire called 'out' as mum started to shout
About the sprout that had landed
In the biscuit of wheat, that was 'Weetabix' branded.
Mum threw a wobbler and Pete had a chuckle,
As I felt the harsh justice of mum's right hand knuckle.
Serves me right.

Aptly Named

I knew a bread maker called Benjamin Baker,
And good ole' Bob Graves was an undertaker.
We'd see Anthony Butcher for all our meat
And Abigail Heel to look after our feet.
Angela Rose was a florist in town,
While the lavatory attendant was old mister Brown.
Jonathan Wrench was a garage mechanic
And I'm sure Stephan Iceberg sailed on the Titanic.
My friend, Andy Carpenter, became a tree surgeon,
While Emile Caviar collected eggs from a sturgeon.
There is a lawyer called Crook,
A banker called Cash,
A fisherman called Hook,
A fireman called Ash,
A grocer called Green,
A plumber called Leek,
A vegetarian called Bean,
And a gardener called Titchmarsh,
Which isn't an apt name, but he is a good gardener.

It's Bostin in Birmingham

It's bostin in Birmingham, we have a real good crack,
Whether we're brown, white, beige, yellow, red, green or black,
Whenever I leave, I can't wait to get back ...
To Birmingham ...

If England's a buffet, then Birmingham's the sandwiches,
Our dialect is music as we speak loads of different languages.
You may laugh and squawk at the way we talk
And you may all wet your pants,
But even kids in Birmingham know,
There is no 'r' in dance.
Our multi cultural qualities are sought by those who lack these
And we taught Willy Wonka a thing or two
About building chocolate factories.
We used to make cars ... though now the future's looking scarier,
'Cause most people down in London
Prefer to get theirs from Bavaria.

So listen up ... pay attention for goodness sake,
You should hear the taunts that we have to take,
Just because of the way us brummies "spake..."
Here in Birmingham ... and the Black Country.

Blowing Off

You could try a crafty sneeze,
Or even try a growling cough,
Though nothing that you try will hide
The smell of someone blowing off.

A Bloke Tried to Sell Me a Time Machine

A bloke tried to sell me a time machine,
He told me that time travel sells,
"But don't take the word of a salesman," he said,
"Just ask that bloke H.G. Wells".

He told me to sit down and strap myself in
And twist the big knob on the right,
"There'll be a bit of a whirring noise
And you may get a bit of a fright".

"You can choose to go forward or backwards in time,
Whichever the one you'd prefer,
You can go back and visit the three wise men,
With the gold, frankincense and the myrrh"

"Forwards is always a bit of a laugh,
You can visit your kids when they're old"
And I bet that the salesman was thinking,
"Another minute and *this* time machine's sold!"

"No thanks mate" I said, "it's just not for me,
It's not something that I'd like to do,
You shouldn't go messing around with time,
Unless your name is Doctor Who".

Shock

Don't fly
your kite
near pylons,
you may
just get
a shock,
especially if
your dad
turns up
in your
mom's best
summer frock.

37

There's No Leopard Like Snow Leopard

When I was five,
A while ago,
A man on the telly said
"Snow...leopard in jeopardy"
I said "Mom can I go...?
To jeopardy, to see the snow leopard-y?"
"No" said mom "You've misunderstood
In jeopardy means 'danger',
It doesn't sound good
For the snow leopard – in jeopardy."
"But why's he in danger?
Is he crossing the road?
Hasn't he learnt to do the green cross code?
He needs his own crossing,
Like a zebra or pelican,
We need to tell people,
Like the man on the telly can."
"No dear," said mom "it's a bit worse than that,
The future looks bleak for the big snowy cat.
It's out of our hands.
There's not much we can do"
But now you know
And I know,
That just isn't true.
Sometimes moms will say things
To keep us kids at bay.
Snow leopard-y in jeopardy ?
We can change that today.

Climbing

Fasten my harness with a rope ...
And hope,
I make it up the slope,
In one piece,
With Candice,
My niece,
Who loves the musical 'Grease',
Which was ironic really.
Because that's what I felt,
Had been spread on the slope.
I hadn't a hope,
Of steadying my grip,
As I started to slip,
On the slope,
Of no hope,
That was covered in grease.
That's the oily stuff,
Not the musical.
Which was just as well,
As there wasn't much room
For the cast of a show.
My limbs said "no",
As my confidence waned
And my weedy arms strained,
To climb up the slope,
That was covered in slime.
Suddenly, it was tea time,
So I went home,
Disappointed,
Again.

Aeroplane

Aeroplane up in the air,
What keeps you flying way up there?
Is it the wind beneath your wings?
Or lots of technological things?
I'm trying to explain it to my mother,
About your fuselage and your rudder
And things that keep you in the sky,
But mother keeps on asking "Why?
You're not getting me up there,
If we were meant to fly, I swear
The Lord would have given us all feathers,
Instead of motorcycle leathers!"
(Mom would always like to race
Her motorbike, at break neck pace!)
So in an act of pure defiance,
I told her it was rocket science.
Which of course, it is.

Christmas Prezzy

It was the Christmas of nineteen seventy seven,
I woke and thought I'd gone to heaven,
Though I wasn't dead – feel free to applaud,
No, I'd just been given my first skateboard.
Now, mom wasn't keen, though my dad had convinced her
(He should've been given a job in Westminster),
That a skateboard would give me hours of fun,
So she agreed to let my dad buy me one.
"But if you come a cropper and graze your knee,
Or if you break your leg, don't come running to me!"
So like every responsible parent should do,
They clipped me round the ear and said
"Use your Christmas money to get some pads and a helmet".

41

My Cousin John

My cousin John is a little bit scary,
He's a little bit tall and a little bit hairy,
When I go round to his I'm a little bit wary
Of my cousin John.

He gets into fights and he doesn't care,
He'll thump your nose and pull your hair,
He'll turn you cold with the weight of his stare,
My cousin John.

He's alright really, my cousin John,
Just depends who's side he's playing on,
If there's two men left then I'd be the one
To pick...my cousin John.

He's grown up now and he's sound as a pound,
His feet are responsibly fixed to the ground,
But don't upset his family when you're around
My cousin John.

My Dad Made a Smell

My dad made a smell, yes, I know it was him,
'Cause he leant slightly forward and started to grin.
He asked if my brother could pull on his finger,
Then out popped a smell that would linger and linger.
My mom told him off for a rude thing like that,
So he blamed it on Fluffy, our family cat.
Now Fluffy could make nasty smells of her own,
Or leave little 'parcels' around our home,
But this one was dad's, he just couldn't hide it,
'Cause the one who denied it,
Was the one who supplied it.

I Met Jesus at St. Andrew's Football Stadium

I met Jesus at St. Andrew's Football Stadium,
He sang 'Keep Right On' with the crowd,
He wiped the sweat from his face,
With his blue and white scarf,
And made it look like the Turin Shroud.
It seemed really apt that one of his saints
Had invited him back to his ground,
To cheer on the team that he'd sponsored,
Though, the ticket cost forty odd pound.
Jesus didn't mind 'cause he had a few quid
And the game was turning into a thriller,
One – nil to Blues with five minutes to go,
As the Blues held on tight with the Villa.
Now, the Villa pushed forward with their 'angel' – Juan Pablo,
His shot rattled hard off the post,
But the Villa couldn't break down the City defence
Of the Father, Son and Holy Ghost.
"This Is getting a bit too close for comfort!", thought Christ,
So our Lord flexed his heavenly will,
He made the Villa back four, fluff it up once more...
Birmingham – 2 , Villa – Nil.
Poor Aston Villa, they stood not a chance
With their team of cads, blaggards and knaves,
They should have stuck our good Lord Jesus in goal,
Because everyone knows – Jesus Saves.

Phil Guise and his X-Ray Eyes

Philip Guise had X-Ray eyes, he could see through things,
He'd sometimes see through people's lies,
Old Philip Guise's X-Ray eyeses.
"Have you seen the toilet frog?
Look down that loo to view it!"
But you couldn't fool Phil's X-Ray eyes,
'Cause he just saw straight through it.
"Phil, I've got an aching arm, it really hurts to poke it!"
"Let's have a look," said X-Ray Phil,
"I think you've gone and broke it".
He did a lot of useful things
Did Phil, with his special sight,
But I recall the day those eyes got Phil into a fight...

Bruiser Bill was six foot three,
His best friend's name was 'mad' Chuck D,
They both had girlfriends, Mel and Sue,
With clothes that you could not see through,
Unless... your name was Phil.
He looked at Mel and Sue and smirked,
His X-Ray eyes, they really worked!
Now, mad Chuck D and bruiser Bill,
Looked on at Phil as he stood still...staring
...through the clothes the girls were wearing,
While Bill and Chuck, with nostrils flaring,
Charged at Phil, who was way past caring,
For he was caught in a naughty trance,
At the sight of the girls with no clothes or pants!
Then the lights went out ... and Phil woke in bed,
With a very sore nose and a very sore head,
Which goes to show that it's not wise,
To stare at girls with your X-Ray eyes.

I Want To Be a Hobbit

I want to be a hobbit,
I want to be nice and short,
Wraiths with rings are not my thing
And goblins are not my sort.
I want to have those pointy ears,
'Cause pointy ears are neat,
I'll save lots of money on socks and shoes,
'Cause I'll have robust, hairy feet.
I want to be the underdog,
When I'm fighting orcs and dragons,
I want to quaff a pint of finest ale,
With my good friend Bilbo Baggins.
I want to take the ring to Mordor
And drop it into Mount Doom's fire,
I want to be called Togo Foxburr of Fair Downs*
Back home in the Shire.
Being a hobbit would make me content,
I'd be really pleased with myself,
Cause being a hobbit would be far less hassle,
Than being, say, a fanciful elf.
It's my image of hell, there in Rivendell,
All that dreamy and long flowing hair,
Imagine all that shampoo and conditioner you'd need,
To keep troublesome lice out of there.
It must get boring living forever,
Life would loose all of it's worth,
So I'll go on long, mischievous journeys,
To spice things up in Middle Earth.
No, a Hobbit's life is the life for me,
Not a man, elf, wizard, nor orc,
So when it's my turn to get born again,
Will someone have a quick word with the stork.

*Hobbit name generated from www.chriswetherell.com/hobbit/

Rabbits Dressed as Chickens

Mom and Dad bought a couple of rabbits,
They did what rabbits do...
So my parents could have a steady supply,
For casseroles, pies and stew.

This wasn't strange for my mom and dad,
As they'd both been brought up on a farm,
Eating rabbits ... amongst other things,
Never did them any harm.

A problem they hadn't considered,
That may have left them with lasting regrets,
Was how to get me and my siblings,
To eat our adorable pets.

We lived quite close to some heath land,
A habitat for foxes and stoats,
So mom and dad seized upon the chance,
To use these creatures as "scape goats".

Under cover of night, to the rabbit compound,
Mom and Dad quietly crept,
To silently despatch a bunny or two,
While all of their offspring slept

Next day at dinner, our sister cried out
"Snowy and Fluffy have gone!"
"It must have been those nasty foxes" said mum,
"A bit more chicken, anyone?"

I Don't Want to Grow Up

I want to get scared when a horror film starts,
I don't want to grow up...
I want to laugh out loud when my brother farts,
I don't want to grow up...
I want to flick bogies behind the teacher's back,
I want to light fires with my best friend, Jack,
I want to say 'poo' and 'bum' and 'cack',
I don't want to grow up.

I want to ride my 'Raleigh Chopper' and graze my knee,
I don't want to grow up...
I want to see how many bubble gums I can get for 50p,
I don't want to grow up...
I want to fast forward to the 'action' scenes,
I don't want to eat cabbage or carrots or greens,
I don't want to flippin' know what 'existentialist' means,
I don't want to grow up.

I want to be like James Bond and do all my own stunts,
I don't want to grow up...
I want to see how many penny chews I can get in my gob at once,
I don't want to grow up...
I want to get a magnifying glass and terrorise ants,
I want to throw a tantrum when I get the chance,
I want to get embarrassed when my mom and dad dance,
I don't want to grow up.

I want to squish potato through the gaps in my teeth,
I don't want to grow up...
I want to lift up rocks to find out what's underneath,
I don't want to grow up...
I want to make a go cart out of bits of wood and junk,
I want to shake my head to some metal and some punk,
I want to grow up fast so I can go out and get drunk...hmmm...
I don't want to grow up.

Cheese Before Bedtime

It's ten thirty – you're peckish,
You know you shouldn't risk it,
But you can't resist some 'Dairylea'
Spread heartily on a biscuit.
Though once you've had a nibble
The urge begins to fester,
So you tuck into crackers with Wensleydale
And a cheeky bit of Red Leicester.
You know this senseless craving is just a reckless folly,
- It's bedtime soon and you've just scoffed
Half of the cheese trolley!
And so – to bed …
Cheese before bedtime? Are you off your head?
You will be …

As the pillows wrestle away your consciousness – it starts,
A cabaret of calamity with curiously cast … bit parts.
Up goes the curtain and down go the lights,
On this dairy dreamtime – it's going to be one of those nights!
First up – Paul McCartney and Madonna
Sharing steak and kidney pies,
While Paris Hilton gets life in prison, just for telling lies.
A naked George W Bush rides bareback on a horse,
While Tony Blair becomes a Jedi,
Just so he can feel the force.
Ken Dodd's dad's dog chases his own tail,
As Chavs and Goths and Emos go swimming with a whale!
The guys from 'Little Britain' say 'I'm a lady' in their dresses,
While the ugly sisters in Cinderella turn out to be princesses.
'Take That' and 'Girls Aloud' do the YMCA dance,
As the west end cast of 'Joseph'
Burst out of Andrew Lloyd Weber's pants!

The hills *literally* come to life, with the sound of Connie Fisher,
While *that* girl from Big Brother turns into an ant
And the whole world lines up to squish her.

At which point ... a shake ...
Brings you back, you're awake ... you sit up and take ...
...a good look around,
"Time to get up" says the dulcet sound
Of the radio alarm.
Woa... cheese before bedtime?
Never did me any harm.

Ashley is a Bon Vivant

Ashley is a "bon vivant",
He likes to "live it large"
He has crumpets for his breakfast,
With butter instead of "marg".
A creamy, warm hot chocolate,
Is his beverage of choice,
He doesn't drive – but if he did,
The car would be a Rolls Royce …
Though…most probably someone else's,
As he lacks that kind of money,
But that doesn't stop him poaching eggs,
With yolks that are nice and runny…
Just right for toasted soldiers,
Cut to a specific width and length,
Accompanied by a sausage … or two…
As the growing lad needs his strength.
His tastes are not extravagant
And he's not a fussy eater,
As long as the food is conducive,
To his penchant for 'La Dolce Vita'.

Didgeri Dave

Didgeri Dave played the didgeridoo,
He took a hot lemon drink,
For the didgeri flu,
He had dumplings and carrots,
In his didgeri stew
And he went to the toilet,
For a didgeri number two.
Now, most days, didgeri Dave
Would get up around eight,
Have tea and toast
On his didgeri plate (though not together on the plate),
He'd go out for a jog
To feel didgeri great,
Though doing all this made him
Didgeri late.
Now, Dave's boss at the office
Was a kind-hearted squire,
Helped people out of the
Didgeri mire,
But today, his temper
Was on didgeri fire
And said "Don't be late again or you're for the high jump!"
Which suited Dave because he was a kangaroo.

The Ballad of Brian the Balloon Dog

Timmy was timid … that's what the grown ups said,
They couldn't figure out what was going on inside his head,
Some said he was weird, while others said "withdrawn",
He'd barely held a conversation since the day that he was born!
His social skills were not what they really could have been,
He didn't have a lot of friends – they were few and far between.
Interaction with his peers and other people wasn't great,
Though life can be a bit like that … when you're eight.

Mom and dad got worried when folk kept on asking "Why?"
"Timmy's such a lovely boy, but he's so very shy.
Perhaps there's someone he could see, if you get our gist,
A special teacher of some sort, or child psychiatrist"

Now mum and dad felt pressurised,
Though Timmy wasn't fussed,
He knew his caring parents were the kind that he could trust.
So instead of getting him seen to, by the men with white coats on,
They sent him to a class mate's party – a friendly lad called John.

The party was a fun affair with cakes and crisps and squash,
They even had some canapés, because John's mum was posh.
A clown called "Cuddles" came along to make the children laugh,
With silly songs and magic tricks, like cutting things in half,
Then ... he'd join them back together, with a few choice magic words,
Or change them into handkerchiefs or even magic birds.
Now, Timmy grinned a quiet grin – his facial muscles flexed,
But nothing had prepared him for what was coming next!

Cuddles reached into his pocket and pulled out something pink,
And when he put it to his lips, it did the opposite of shrink.
It inflated like a long sausage - Cuddles knotted it at the end
And when he'd made another two he began to weave and bend ...
The rubber sausages together, they squeaked with every twist,
He wrestled with his creation and with a flick of his skilful wrist
He produced a party piece that beat his tricks and silly tunes...
Tim looked in awe, as what he saw, was a dog made from balloons.

When Cuddles asked, "Who'd like this dog?"
Tim's hand shot straight up,
After all, he'd watched that cute thing grow, ever since it was a pup.
Everyone's hands were in the air, Timmy thought he'd lost his chance,
Then Cuddles pointed Timmy out and asked him to advance.
Timmy wasn't sure at first, this was quite a step for him,
Especially as he'd have to pass two brothers, both of whom looked grim.
He took a deep breath ... and strode to the front, as confident as a lion.
"Would you like to name your dog" asked Cuddles, "Yes" said Tim,
"He's Brian".

Timmy was so excited, he couldn't wait for the party to end,
So he could race back to his mum and dad, with his new found friend.
He politely thanked John and his mum for such a celebration,
Then headed off home with Brian, his dog / balloon creation.
Tim's mum and dad were really chuffed,
They couldn't believe their ears
Timmy talked and talked about Brian,
It was the most he'd said in years!
They were so pleased that Brian had brought Timmy out of his shell,
Even though he was pink with a rubber coat
And absolutely no sense of smell.

Brian and Tim became best pals, they looked out for each other,
He was more than just a balloon dog ...
Brian was like Timmy's brother ...
And when they went out to the park, they ran and jumped and played,
And when they went swimming,
Brian doubled up as Timmy's buoyancy aid.

58

The safari park was a popular haunt,
They'd look at the Yaks and Baboons,
Wondering what the place would be like,
If the animals were made of balloons.
Giraffes weren't hard to imagine – Elephants were harder to figure,
Wolves were easy – they'd be like Brian, only a little bit bigger.

Tim's mum and dad couldn't be more pleased,
They were happy and elated,
But how would Tim react, if Brian the balloon dog became deflated?
They could see that Timmy got anxious,
When he heard a hiss or a squeak,
He'd examine Brian's rubber limbs, just in case he'd sprung a leak.

Timmy took precautions to defend against balloon dog disasters,
He always carried a puncture kit, complete with packs of plasters.
But he knew that it was inevitable, even with Tim's special care,
That like every man who had ever gone bald ...
Brian would loose his air.

That day would come at the local pub,
It was called the Bull and Gate,
Tim's dad was in the darts team –
You could say they were tempting fate.
Tim's dad was onto a winner, he just needed double top,
But little did they know that final dart,
Would be the one to make Brian pop!

That dart, it bounced off the wire and ricocheted into the sky,
It twisted a new trajectory and made straight for Timmy's eye!
Brian the Balloon dog burst into life, to deflect that rogue of a dart
And before anyone could do anything,
It pierced him right through the heart.

Brian went out in a glorious "BANG!"...
The balloon dog was no more,
All that was left were pink fragments, scattered all over the floor.
Timmy's eyes filled with tears, his grief too hard to hide,
Yet while his woe ran down his cheeks, his heart was full of pride,
Brian had brought about a change that no dart could destroy,
He'd helped a timid Timmy become a confident young boy.

Now ...
Whenever Tim's under the weather,
There's one thing that clears the fog
And that's the memory of his bestest friend ...
Brian the balloon dog.

Glossary

Some words or terms I've used that you may not understand, or bits of interesting information, are explained here ... after all, that's what a "glossary" is.

Page 9 "Faggots and 'pays'" is the Brummie / Black Country pronunciation of "Faggots and Peas", a dish that many people from the area enjoyed (and still do!)

Page 9 "Enoch Powell" was the conservative M.P. for Wolverhampton South West from 1950 to 1974. Probably his most famous speech was his "Rivers of Blood" speech which he gave in Birmingham in 1968 speaking out against immigration. In my opinion, a horrible man.

Page 9 "kiddies milk snatcher" ... Margaret Thatcher, British Prime Minister 1979-1990, was nicknamed (amongst other things), "The milk snatcher" after stopping free milk for school children at school during her reign.

Page 26 "Roger Daltrey" lead singer with rock band "The Who", who did a song called "My Generation".

Page 29 "Vidal Sassoon" was (and still is) a very famous hair-dresser

Page 31 "Wee willie winkie" is an old Scottish nursery rhyme by William Miller.

Page 36 "bostin" is a Brummie / Black Country word meaning "brilliant"

Page 36 "The Black Country" is an area next to Birmingham, loosely comprising of Walsall, Dudley, Sandwell and Wolverhampton districts.

Page 36 "spake" is a Brummie / Black Country pronunciation for "speak".

Page 43 "Keep Right On" as in "Keep Right On to the End of the Road", a song by Harry Lauder which was adopted by Birmingham City fans as their 'anthem'.

Page 43 "...their angel, Juan Pablo" refers to Juan Pablo Angel Arango, a Columbian striker who played for Aston Villa from 2001 to 2007

Page 54 "A Bon Vivant" is someone who likes the finer things in life. It's one of those French phrases that's used in the English language, like "piece de resistance".

Page 54 "La Dolce Vita". Italian this time (multi lingual, me!). It translates to "The Sweet Life".

Page 56 "the men with white coats on" ... doctors—usually the ones who look after people with mental issues.

That's about it for this glossary. If there are any other bits 'n' bobs that don't make sense,, or there's any words you don't understand, then look them up in a dictionary or pop into your local library and have a look on the internet.

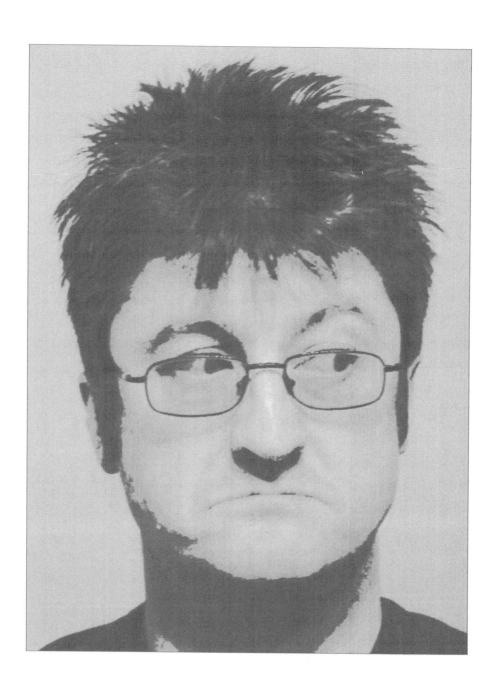

A Bit About the Author ... Spoz

SPOZ...was born at 44 Kineton Road, Rubery, on the edge of Birmingham in 1964. He became known as 'Spoz' (like his brothers and sister) because it was easier than his real name, 'GIOVANNI ESPOSITO' and happens to be the bit between the 'E' and the 'ito' (sort of).

SPOZ...is an award winning performance poet, singer / songwriter, film maker, playwright, carp re-upholsterer and is the poet-in-residence at Birmingham City FC. He has been seen on BBC and Central Television, has written for, and been heard on BBC Radio Four, Radio Five Live, Radio West Midlands, Radio Coventry & Warwickshire, Capital Gold and on the toilet. Spoz has performed at the Glastonbury festival, Cheltenham Literature festival, Oxford Literature Festival, Warwick Words festival, Ledbury Poetry Festival, Bartons Arms Comedy Club, the Shambala festival and in front of his mom.

SPOZ...was 'crowned' Birmingham's eleventh poet laureate in October 2006. He continues to work extensively in schools, lifting the appeal of writing and performing poetry to hitherto, unseen heights.

SPOZ... remains modest and still lives in Birmingham.

SPOZ ... looks a bit like Joe Pasquale.

This is a list of people who have inspired me, influenced me or helped me in anyway (whether they know it or not). So allow me to say "thank you".

Mama e Papa e la famiglia Esposito
Dreadlockalien
Elvis McGonagall
AF Harrold
John Hegley
John Cooper Clarke
Attila the Stockbroker
Roz Goddard
Everyone at Birmingham Libraries
Arts Council (West Midlands)
Birmingham Book Communications
Carl Thompson
Colin Faulkner
Paul Hill
Rachael Pantechnicon
Marcus and Sara-Jane
Apples and Snakes
Polar Bear, Kim, Dan, Evoke, Sean, Big Al, Si, Charlie, Maggie, Roy, Lorna, Moquapi, Emma, Duble, Matt, Big Bren, Rafael and all my poetry friends in and around Brum.
All the young people I've met at all the schools I've ever done (and yet to do) poetry workshops at.
Birmingham, Worcestershire, Warwickshire, Sandwell, Dudley and all the other LA's who've placed their trust in me.
Everyone I met at Glastonbury 2005
Carl Chinn and Jimmy Franks
Andrea H, Janice B, Gemma C, Juliet F, Carol M and Jan D.
All my teachers at St. James RC Primary School in Rubery
All my teachers at Archbishop Masterson's RC Secondary School in Northfield (now demolished).
All my ex-colleagues at MG Rover, in all it's incarnations.

...and anyone else who knows me.

Here's the last page...

...and here's the other side of the last page.